G000037245

Japanese Dress
Diary 2021

V&A Publishing

First published by V&A Publishing, 2020
Victoria and Albert Museum
South Kensington
London SW7 2RL

Discover more at
vam.ac.uk/publishing

© Victoria and Albert Museum, London

Pocket edition
ISBN 978 1 85177 982 6

A catalogue record for this book is
available from the British Library.

Every effort has been made to seek permission to
reproduce those images whose copyright does not
reside with the V&A, and we are grateful to the
individuals and institutions who have assisted in this
task. Any omissions are entirely unintentional, and
the details should be addressed to V&A Publishing.

Printed in China

Please note that lunar festivals marked in
calendar may be subject to change and tha
religious holiday dates can vary according
local or regional customs.

Museum Information

Victoria and Albert Museum
South Kensington
London SW7 2RL

Visiting the Museum
vam.ac.uk/visit

What's On
vam.ac.uk/whatson

History of the Museum
vam.ac.uk/history

Search the Collections
vam.ac.uk/collections

Study Rooms
vam.ac.uk/info/study-rooms

Archives
vam.ac.uk/archives

National Art Library
vam.ac.uk/nal

V&A Shop
vam.ac.uk/shop

V&A Membership
vam.ac.uk/membership

V&A Publishing

Supporting the world's leading
museum of art and design,
the Victoria and Albert
Museum, London

2021

JANUARY
M	T	W	T	F	S	S
				1	2	3
4	5	6	7	8	9	10
11	12	13	14	15	16	17
18	19	20	21	22	23	24
25	26	27	28	29	30	31

FEBRUARY
M	T	W	T	F	S	S
1	2	3	4	5	6	7
8	9	10	11	12	13	14
15	16	17	18	19	20	21
22	23	24	25	26	27	28

MARCH
M	T	W	T	F	S	S
1	2	3	4	5	6	7
8	9	10	11	12	13	14
15	16	17	18	19	20	21
22	23	24	25	26	27	28
29	30	31				

APRIL
M	T	W	T	F	S	S
			1	2	3	4
5	6	7	8	9	10	11
12	13	14	15	16	17	18
19	20	21	22	23	24	25
26	27	28	29	30		

MAY
M	T	W	T	F	S	S
					1	2
3	4	5	6	7	8	9
10	11	12	13	14	15	16
17	18	19	20	21	22	23
24	25	26	27	28	29	30
31						

JUNE
M	T	W	T	F	S	S
	1	2	3	4	5	6
7	8	9	10	11	12	13
14	15	16	17	18	19	20
21	22	23	24	25	26	27
28	29	30				

JULY
M	T	W	T	F	S	S
			1	2	3	4
5	6	7	8	9	10	11
12	13	14	15	16	17	18
19	20	21	22	23	24	25
26	27	28	29	30	31	

AUGUST
M	T	W	T	F	S	S
						1
2	3	4	5	6	7	8
9	10	11	12	13	14	15
16	17	18	19	20	21	22
23	24	25	26	27	28	29
30	31					

SEPTEMBER
M	T	W	T	F	S	S
		1	2	3	4	5
6	7	8	9	10	11	12
13	14	15	16	17	18	19
20	21	22	23	24	25	26
27	28	29	30			

OCTOBER
M	T	W	T	F	S	S
				1	2	3
4	5	6	7	8	9	10
11	12	13	14	15	16	17
18	19	20	21	22	23	24
25	26	27	28	29	30	31

NOVEMBER
M	T	W	T	F	S	S
1	2	3	4	5	6	7
8	9	10	11	12	13	14
15	16	17	18	19	20	21
22	23	24	25	26	27	28
29	30					

DECEMBER
M	T	W	T	F	S	S
		1	2	3	4	5
6	7	8	9	10	11	12
13	14	15	16	17	18	19
20	21	22	23	24	25	26
27	28	29	30	31		

2022

JANUARY
M	T	W	T	F	S	S
					1	2
3	4	5	6	7	8	9
10	11	12	13	14	15	16
17	18	19	20	21	22	23
24	25	26	27	28	29	30
31						

FEBRUARY
M	T	W	T	F	S	S
	1	2	3	4	5	6
7	8	9	10	11	12	13
14	15	16	17	18	19	20
21	22	23	24	25	26	27
28						

MARCH
M	T	W	T	F	S	S
	1	2	3	4	5	6
7	8	9	10	11	12	13
14	15	16	17	18	19	20
21	22	23	24	25	26	27
28	29	30	31			

APRIL
M	T	W	T	F	S	S
				1	2	3
4	5	6	7	8	9	10
11	12	13	14	15	16	17
18	19	20	21	22	23	24
25	26	27	28	29	30	

MAY
M	T	W	T	F	S	S
						1
2	3	4	5	6	7	8
9	10	11	12	13	14	15
16	17	18	19	20	21	22
23	24	25	26	27	28	29
30	31					

JUNE
M	T	W	T	F	S	S
		1	2	3	4	5
6	7	8	9	10	11	12
13	14	15	16	17	18	19
20	21	22	23	24	25	26
27	28	29	30			

JULY
M	T	W	T	F	S	S
				1	2	3
4	5	6	7	8	9	10
11	12	13	14	15	16	17
18	19	20	21	22	23	24
25	26	27	28	29	30	31

AUGUST
M	T	W	T	F	S	S
1	2	3	4	5	6	7
8	9	10	11	12	13	14
15	16	17	18	19	20	21
22	23	24	25	26	27	28
29	30	31				

SEPTEMBER
M	T	W	T	F	S	S
			1	2	3	4
5	6	7	8	9	10	11
12	13	14	15	16	17	18
19	20	21	22	23	24	25
26	27	28	29	30		

OCTOBER
M	T	W	T	F	S	S
					1	2
3	4	5	6	7	8	9
10	11	12	13	14	15	16
17	18	19	20	21	22	23
24	25	26	27	28	29	30
31						

NOVEMBER
M	T	W	T	F	S	S
	1	2	3	4	5	6
7	8	9	10	11	12	13
14	15	16	17	18	19	20
21	22	23	24	25	26	27
28	29	30				

DECEMBER
M	T	W	T	F	S	S
			1	2	3	4
5	6	7	8	9	10	11
12	13	14	15	16	17	18
19	20	21	22	23	24	25
26	27	28	29	30	31	

MONDAY

21

TUESDAY

22

WEDNESDAY

23

THURSDAY

24

Christmas Eve

FRIDAY

25

Christmas Day
Holiday UK, IRL, USA,
CAN, AUS, NZL

SATURDAY

26

Boxing Day
Holiday UK, AUS (most regions), NZL
St Stephen's Day
Holiday IRL

SUNDAY

27

DECEMBER / JANUARY

MONDAY

28

Holiday UK, AUS, NZL

TUESDAY

29

WEDNESDAY

30

THURSDAY

31

New Year's Eve

FRIDAY

1

New Year's Day
Holiday UK, IRL, USA,
CAN, AUS, NZL

SATURDAY

2

SUNDAY

3

JANUARY

MONDAY
4

Holiday SCO, NZL

TUESDAY
5

WEDNESDAY
6

THURSDAY
7

FRIDAY
8

SATURDAY
9

SUNDAY
10

JANUARY

MONDAY
11

TUESDAY
12

WEDNESDAY
13

THURSDAY
14

FRIDAY
15

SATURDAY
16

SUNDAY
17

MONDAY

18

Martin Luther King Jr. Day
Holiday USA

TUESDAY

19

WEDNESDAY

20

THURSDAY

21

FRIDAY

22

SATURDAY

23

SUNDAY

24

JANUARY

MONDAY
25

Burns Night

TUESDAY
26

Australia Day
AUS

WEDNESDAY
27

THURSDAY
28

FRIDAY
29

SATURDAY
30

SUNDAY
31

FEBRUARY

MONDAY
1

TUESDAY
2

WEDNESDAY
3

THURSDAY
4

FRIDAY
5

SATURDAY
6

Waitangi Day
Holiday NZ

SUNDAY
7

FEBRUARY

MONDAY
8
Waitangi Day Observed
Holiday NZL

TUESDAY
9

WEDNESDAY
10

THURSDAY
11

FRIDAY
12
Chinese New Year

SATURDAY
13

SUNDAY
14
St Valentine's Day

MONDAY

15

Presidents' Day
Holiday USA (most states)

TUESDAY

16

Shrove Tuesday

WEDNESDAY

17

THURSDAY

18

FRIDAY

19

SATURDAY

20

SUNDAY

21

FEBRUARY

MONDAY
22

TUESDAY
23

WEDNESDAY
24

THURSDAY
25

FRIDAY
26

SATURDAY
27

SUNDAY
28

MARCH

MONDAY

1

St David's Day

TUESDAY

2

WEDNESDAY

3

THURSDAY

4

FRIDAY

5

SATURDAY

6

SUNDAY

7

MARCH

MONDAY
8

TUESDAY
9

WEDNESDAY
10

THURSDAY
11

FRIDAY
12

SATURDAY
13

SUNDAY
14

Mother's Day
UK

Daylight Saving Time begins
USA, CAN

MONDAY

15

TUESDAY

16

WEDNESDAY

17

St Patrick's Day
Holiday NIR, IRL

THURSDAY

18

FRIDAY

19

SATURDAY

20

March Equinox

SUNDAY

21

MARCH

MONDAY
22

TUESDAY
23

WEDNESDAY
24

THURSDAY
25

FRIDAY
26

SATURDAY
27

SUNDAY
28

British Summer Time begins
First day of Passover

MONDAY

29

TUESDAY

30

WEDNESDAY

31

THURSDAY

1

Good Friday
Holiday UK, CAN,
AUS, NZL

FRIDAY

2

SATURDAY

3

Easter Sunday
Daylight Saving Time ends
AUS, NZL
Last day of Passover

SUNDAY

4

APRIL

MONDAY
5

Easter Monday
Holiday UK (not SCO),
IRL, AUS, NZL

TUESDAY
6

WEDNESDAY
7

THURSDAY
8

FRIDAY
9

SATURDAY
10

SUNDAY
11

MONDAY

12

TUESDAY

13

Ramadan begins

WEDNESDAY

14

THURSDAY

15

FRIDAY

16

SATURDAY

17

SUNDAY

18

APRIL

MONDAY
19

TUESDAY
20

WEDNESDAY
21

THURSDAY
22

FRIDAY
23

St George's Day

SATURDAY
24

SUNDAY
25

ANZAC Day
Holiday AUS (not NT, WA), NZ

MONDAY

26

ANZAC Day Observed
Holiday most of AUS, NZL

TUESDAY

27

WEDNESDAY

28

THURSDAY

29

FRIDAY

30

SATURDAY

1

SUNDAY

2

MAY

MONDAY

3

Early May Bank Holiday
UK, IRL

TUESDAY

4

WEDNESDAY

5

THURSDAY

6

FRIDAY

7

SATURDAY

8

SUNDAY

9

Mother's Day
USA, CAN, AUS, NZL

MAY

MONDAY
10

TUESDAY
11

WEDNESDAY
12

THURSDAY
13

Ramadan ends

FRIDAY
14

SATURDAY
15

SUNDAY
16

MONDAY
17

TUESDAY
18

WEDNESDAY
19

THURSDAY
20

FRIDAY
21

SATURDAY
22

SUNDAY
23

MONDAY

24

Victoria Day
Holiday CAN (not NS, PE, QC)

TUESDAY

25

WEDNESDAY

26

THURSDAY

27

FRIDAY

28

SATURDAY

29

SUNDAY

30

MAY / JUNE

MONDAY
31

Spring Bank Holiday
UK

Memorial Day
Holiday USA

TUESDAY
1

WEDNESDAY
2

THURSDAY
3

FRIDAY
4

SATURDAY
5

SUNDAY
6

June Bank Holiday
IRL

Queen's Birthday
Holiday NZL

MONDAY
7

TUESDAY
8

WEDNESDAY
9

THURSDAY
10

FRIDAY
11

SATURDAY
12

SUNDAY
13

JUNE

MONDAY
14

TUESDAY
15

WEDNESDAY
16

THURSDAY
17

FRIDAY
18

SATURDAY
19

SUNDAY
20

Father's Day
UK, IRL, USA, CAN

葛飾俗美人姿

MONDAY
21

June Solstice

TUESDAY
22

WEDNESDAY
23

THURSDAY
24

FRIDAY
25

SATURDAY
26

SUNDAY
27

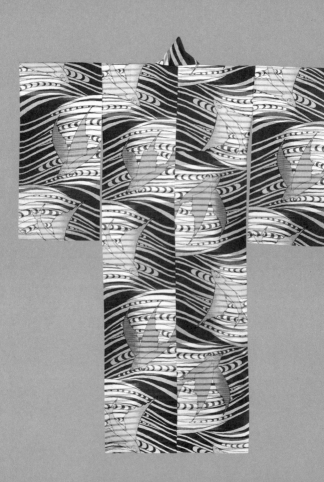

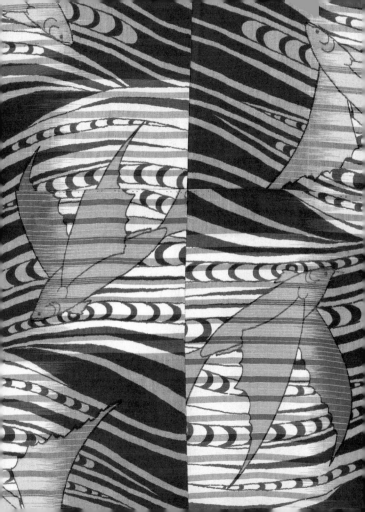

MONDAY
28

TUESDAY
29

WEDNESDAY
30

THURSDAY
1

Canada Day
Holiday CAN

FRIDAY
2

SATURDAY
3

SUNDAY
4

Independence Day
Holiday USA

JULY

MONDAY
5

Independence Day Observed
Holiday USA

TUESDAY
6

WEDNESDAY
7

THURSDAY
8

FRIDAY
9

SATURDAY
10

SUNDAY
11

JULY

MONDAY
12

Battle of the Boyne
Holiday NIR

TUESDAY
13

WEDNESDAY
14

THURSDAY
15

FRIDAY
16

SATURDAY
17

SUNDAY
18

MONDAY
19

TUESDAY
20

WEDNESDAY
21

THURSDAY
22

FRIDAY
23

SATURDAY
24

SUNDAY
25

MONDAY

26

TUESDAY

27

WEDNESDAY

28

THURSDAY

29

FRIDAY

30

SATURDAY

31

SUNDAY

1

MONDAY

2

Summer Bank Holiday
SCO, IRL

TUESDAY

3

WEDNESDAY

4

THURSDAY

5

FRIDAY

6

SATURDAY

7

SUNDAY

8

AUGUST

MONDAY

9

TUESDAY

10

Islamic New Year

WEDNESDAY

11

THURSDAY

12

FRIDAY

13

SATURDAY

14

SUNDAY

15

AUGUST

MONDAY
16

TUESDAY
17

WEDNESDAY
18

THURSDAY
19

FRIDAY
20

SATURDAY
21

SUNDAY
22

MONDAY
23

TUESDAY
24

WEDNESDAY
25

THURSDAY
26

FRIDAY
27

SATURDAY
28

SUNDAY
29

25

MONDAY

30

Summer Bank Holiday
UK (not SCO)

TUESDAY

31

WEDNESDAY

1

THURSDAY

2

FRIDAY

3

SATURDAY

4

SUNDAY

5

Father's Day
AUS, NZL

SEPTEMBER

MONDAY
6

Labour Day
Holiday USA, CAN

TUESDAY
7

WEDNESDAY
8

THURSDAY
9

FRIDAY
10

SATURDAY
11

SUNDAY
12

MONDAY

13

TUESDAY

14

WEDNESDAY

15

THURSDAY

16

Yom Kippur

FRIDAY

17

SATURDAY

18

SUNDAY

19

SEPTEMBER

MONDAY
20

TUESDAY
21

WEDNESDAY
22

September Equinox

THURSDAY
23

FRIDAY
24

SATURDAY
25

SUNDAY
26

Daylight Saving Time begin
NZ

MONDAY

27

TUESDAY

28

WEDNESDAY

29

THURSDAY

30

FRIDAY

1

SATURDAY

2

SUNDAY

3

Daylight Saving Time begins
AUS

OCTOBER

MONDAY
4

TUESDAY
5

WEDNESDAY
6

THURSDAY
7

FRIDAY
8

SATURDAY
9

SUNDAY
10

MONDAY
11

Columbus Day
Holiday most of USA
Thanksgiving Day
Holiday most of CAN

TUESDAY
12

WEDNESDAY
13

THURSDAY
14

FRIDAY
15

SATURDAY
16

SUNDAY
17

OCTOBER

MONDAY
18

TUESDAY
19

WEDNESDAY
20

THURSDAY
21

FRIDAY
22

SATURDAY
23

SUNDAY
24

MONDAY

25

October Bank Holiday
IRL
Labour Day
Holiday NZL

TUESDAY

26

WEDNESDAY

27

THURSDAY

28

FRIDAY

29

SATURDAY

30

SUNDAY

31

Hallowe'en
British Summer Time ends

NOVEMBER

MONDAY

1

TUESDAY

2

WEDNESDAY

3

THURSDAY

4

Diwali

FRIDAY

5

Guy Fawkes Night

SATURDAY

6

SUNDAY

7

Daylight Saving Time ends
USA, CAN

MONDAY

8

TUESDAY

9

WEDNESDAY

10

THURSDAY

11

Veterans Day
Holiday USA
Remembrance Day
Holiday most of CAN

FRIDAY

12

SATURDAY

13

SUNDAY

14

Remembrance Sunday
UK

NOVEMBER

MONDAY
15

TUESDAY
16

WEDNESDAY
17

THURSDAY
18

FRIDAY
19

SATURDAY
20

SUNDAY
21

MONDAY

22

TUESDAY

23

WEDNESDAY

24

THURSDAY

Thanksgiving
Holiday USA

25

FRIDAY

26

SATURDAY

27

SUNDAY

First Day of Advent

28

NOVEMBER / DECEMBER

MONDAY

29

TUESDAY

30

St Andrew's Day
Holiday SCO

WEDNESDAY

1

THURSDAY

2

FRIDAY

3

SATURDAY

4

SUNDAY

5

MONDAY

6

TUESDAY

7

WEDNESDAY

8

THURSDAY

9

FRIDAY

10

SATURDAY

11

SUNDAY

12

DECEMBER

MONDAY
13

TUESDAY
14

WEDNESDAY
15

THURSDAY
16

FRIDAY
17

SATURDAY
18

SUNDAY
19

DECEMBER

MONDAY
20

TUESDAY
21

December Solstice

WEDNESDAY
22

THURSDAY
23

FRIDAY
24

Christmas Eve
Holiday USA, CAN

SATURDAY
25

Christmas Day
Holiday UK, IRL, USA,
CAN, AUS, NZL

SUNDAY
26

Boxing Day
Holiday UK, most of AUS, NZL
St Stephen's Day
Holiday IRL

MONDAY

27

Holiday UK, AUS, NZL

TUESDAY

28

Holiday UK, AUS, NZL

WEDNESDAY

29

THURSDAY

30

FRIDAY

31

New Year's Eve
Holiday USA

SATURDAY

1

New Year's Day
Holiday UK, IRL, USA
CAN, AUS, NZL

SUNDAY

2

Illustrations

Images are all colour prints from woodblocks unless otherwise stated. They have been included as details and in some places have been modified.

COVER
The Upper Reaches of the Tama Water Supply Flowing through the Koganei Embankment
Utagawa Hiroshige (1797–1858)
Colour fan print from woodblocks
Japan, 1857
E.12082-1886

DECEMBER
Changing Clothes from the series *Chiyoda Inner Palace*
Yōshū Chikanobu (1838–1912)
Japan, 1895
E.460:49–1951

The Actor Bandō Shūka I as Azumaji
Utagawa Kunisada (1786–1864)
Japan, 1840s
E.14733:64–1886

JANUARY
Hokushi from the series *the Ten Great Pupils of the Haikai Poet Matsuo Bashō*
Utagawa Kunisada (1786–1864)
Japan, 1843–7
E.6060–1916

The Wedding Colour Alteration Ceremony
Utagawa Kuniyoshi (1798–1861)
Japan, 1843–7
E.11465A/1–1886

Design for kimono
Plain weave silk, freehand paste-resist dyeing, hand-painting in ink and colours, embroidery in silk and gold-wrapped silk threads
Probably Kyoto, c.1900
E.712–1901

The Hour of the Snake from the series *Twelve Hours with Genji*
Utagawa Kunisada (1786–1864)
Japan, 1859
E.9404–1886

Kimono
Sudo Reiko (b.1953) for the Isesaki Contemporary Double Ikat Meisen Project

Machine-spun plain weave pongee silk, stencil dyeing of warps and wefts
Isesaki, 2016–18
FE.172–2019
Given by the Isesaki Contemporary Double Ikat Meisen Project

FEBRUARY
Plum Blossoms under Snow at Night
Utagawa Kuniyoshi (1798–1861)
Japan, 1846–8
E.11614:2–1886

Parading Courtesan with Attendants
Utagawa Kunisada (1786–1864)
Japan, 1830s
E.5550:5–1886

MARCH
Prosperous Household and Modern Girls
Utagawa Kunisada (1786–1864)
Japan, 1843–7
E.8335A–1886

Courtesan and Attendants of the Kado-Ebiya House
Utagawa Kunisada (1786–1864)
Japan, 1830s
E.8356:1–1886

An Array of Flowers, Beauties and Famous Places
Ogata Gekkō (1859–1920)
Japan, 1895
E.352–1901

Outer kimono for a woman
Crepe silk, freehand paste-resist dyeing, stencil-dyeing, hand-painting in ink, embroidery in silk and gold-wrapped silk threads
Probably Kyoto, 1860–1900
T.389–1910
Murray Bequest

APRIL
Ladies-in-waiting with Male Entertainers in Female Attire
Utagawa Toyokuni (1769–1825)
Japan, c.1825
E.12642–1886

Fan Seller and Courtesan
Kawamata Tsunemasa
(active 1716–48)
Hanging scroll: ink, colours

and gold on silk
Japan, 1730–48
E.1472-1916

Cherry Blossoms at Night in the Garden from the series *Chiyoda Inner Palace*
Yōshū Chikanobu (1838–1912)
Japan, 1896
E.460:14–1951

The Upper Reaches of the Tama Water Supply Flowing through the Koganei Embankment
Utagawa Hiroshige (1797–1858)
Colour fan print from woodblocks
Japan, 1857
E.12082-1886

MAY
The Fifth Month: Flower Arranging Contest
Utagawa Kunisada (1786–1864)
Japan, 1854
E.8996–1886

Outer kimono for a woman
Crepe silk, freehand paste-resist dyeing, embroidery in gold-wrapped silk threads
Probably Kyoto, 1750–1800
T.64–1954
Given by Mrs Sydney Avis

Cloth-fulling at the Tama River in Settsu Province
Utagawa Kuniyoshi (1798–1861)
Japan, 1847–8
E.10576–1886

Girl Playing with a Doll and Cat
Utagawa Kunisada (1786–1864)
Japan, 1830s
E.5568–1886

JUNE
Kyoriku from the series *the Ten Great Pupils of the Haikai Poet Matsuo Bashō*
Utagawa Kunisada (1786–1864)
Japan, 1843–7
E.6064–1916

Stars from the series *Sun, Moon and Stars*
Utagawa Kunisada (1786–1864)
Japan, c.1830
E.8159–1886

Fashionable Beauty in Summer
Kikukawa Eizan (1787–1867)
Japan, c.1820
E.3777–1953

Kimono for a woman
Machine-spun plain weave pongee
silk, stencil dyeing of warp and
weft threads, supplementary
silver threads
Possibly Isesaki, 1920–30
FE.47–2014

JULY

Design for kimono
Plain weave silk, freehand
paste-resist dyeing, hand-painting
in ink and colours
Probably Kyoto, c.1900
E.736–1901

Stars from the series
Sun, Moon and Stars
Utagawa Kunisada (1786–1864)
Japan, c.1830
E.8159–1886

Theatre District Dawn Moon
Tsukioka Yoshitoshi (1839–92)
Japan, 1886
E.1005–1914

AUGUST

Beauties at Famous Places
Ogata Gekkō (1859–1920)
Japan, 1897
E.354–1901

Wa from the series
Instructive Index of Proverbs
Utagawa Kuniyoshi (1798–1861)
Japan, 1843–7
E.6102–1916

Kimono for a woman
Plain-weave ramie, stencil
imitation tie-dyeing, embroidery
in silk and gold-wrapped
silk thread
Probably Kyoto, 1800–50
CIRC.122–1914

Oshichi of the Yaoya House
Kitagawa Utamaro (1753–1806)
Japan, c.1800
E.427–1895

SEPTEMBER

Beauties at Famous Places
Ogata Gekkō (1859–1920)
Japan, 1897
E.354–1901

*The Wedding Colour
Alteration Ceremony*
Utagawa Kuniyoshi (1798–1861)
Japan, 1843–7
E.11465A/2–1886

Making Thick Tea from the series
Daily Practice of the Tea Ceremony
Mizuno Toshikata (1866–1908)
Japan, 1896–97
E.3131–1905

*Bush Clover at the Tama River
in Ōmi Province*
Utagawa Kuniyoshi (1798–1861)
Japan, 1847–8
E.10573:1–1886

OCTOBER

Kimono for a woman
Figured satin silk, hand-painting
in ink, stencil imitation tie-dyeing,
embroidery in silk and
gold-wrapped silk thread
Probably Kyoto, 1780–1820
FE.19–1986

Gathering Mushrooms in Mid-Autumn
Utagawa Kunisada (1786–1864)
Japan, 1843–7
E.6076–1916

The Garden in the Tenth Month
Utagawa Sadahide (1807–1873)
Japan, 1843–7
E.12223–1886

NOVEMBER

Tonosawa from the series *Depictions
of the Seven Hot Springs of Hakone*
Utagawa Hiroshige (1797–1858)
Colour fan print from woodblocks
Japan, 1847–50
E.4847–1919

*Scene from the Play Travelling to the
East Along the Fifty-Three Stations*
Utagawa Kunisada (1786–1864)
Japan, 1854
E.6201–1886

Design for kimono
Plain weave silk, freehand paste-resist
dyeing, hand-painting in ink
and colours, embroidery in silk and
gold-wrapped silk threads
Probably Kyoto, c.1900
E.706–1901

Robe for Nō theatre
Polychrome figured silk
Kyoto, 1750–1850
T.297–1963
Given by Mrs Edmund de Rothschild

*Bush Clover at the Tama River
in Ōmi Province*
Utagawa Kuniyoshi (1798–1861)
Japan, 1847–8
E.10573:3–1886

*Nakano Street in the
Yoshiwara District of Edo*
Utagawa Hiroshige II (1826–69)
Japan, 1857
E.3928:1–1886

DECEMBER

Snow
Katsukawa Shunsen (1762–1830)
Japan, 1810s
E.12549–1886

The Garden in the Tenth Month
Utagawa Sadahide (1807–1873)
Japan, 1843–7
E.12223–1886

*Fashionable Brocade Patterns
of the Imperial Palace*
Utagawa Kunisada (1786–1864)
Japan, 1847–52
CIRC.636–1962

The Hour of the Snake from the
series *Twelve Hours with Genji*
Utagawa Kunisada (1786–1864)
Japan, 1859
E.9404–1886

Outer kimono for a woman
Satin silk, embroidery in silk and
metallic thread appliqué
Probably Kyoto, 1860–80
FE.73–2014

Notes